S0-ARN-879

Common Core

Standards for Mathematical Content

Domain Number and Operations in Base Ten

Cluster Work with numbers 11–19 to gain foundations for place value.

Standard K.NBT.1

Standards for Mathematical Practice

- ✔ Make sense of problems and persevere in solving them.
- ✔ Reason abstractly and quantitatively.
- ✔ Construct viable arguments and critique the reasoning of others.
- ✔ Model with mathematics.
- ✔ Use appropriate tools strategically.
- ✔ Attend to precision.
- ✔ Look for and make use of structure.
- ✔ Look for and express regularity in repeated reasoning.

Decomposing Numbers 11 to 19

Copyright © 2012 by Pearson Education, Inc., or its affiliates. All Rights Reserved. Printed in the United States of America. This publication is protected by copyright, and permission should be obtained from the publisher prior to any prohibited reproduction, storage in a retrieval system, or transmission in any form or by any means, electronic, mechanical, photocopying, recording, or likewise. For information regarding permissions, write to Rights Management & Contracts, Pearson Education, Inc., One Lake Street, Upper Saddle River, New Jersey 07458.

Pearson, Scott Foresman, Pearson Scott Foresman, and enVisionMATH are trademarks, in the U.S. and/or in other countries, of Pearson Education Inc., or its affiliates.

Common Core State Standards: © Copyright 2010. National Governors Association Center for Best Practices and Council of Chief State School Officers. All rights reserved.

"Understanding by Design" is registered as a trademark with the United States Patent and Trademark Office by the Association for Supervision of Curriculum Development (ASCD). ASCD claims exclusive trademark rights in the terms "Understanding by Design" and the abbreviation "UbD".

Pearson Education has incorporated the concepts of the Understanding by Design methodology into this text in consultation with [contributing author/editor] Grant Wiggins, [one of the] creator[s] of the Understanding by Design methodology. The Association for Supervision of Curriculum Development (ASCD), publisher of the "Understanding by Design Handbook" co-authored by Grant Wiggins, has not authorized, approved or sponsored this work and is in no way affiliated with Pearson or its products.

ISBN-13: 978-0-328-67333-9
ISBN-10: 0-328-67333-1

5 6 7 8 9 10   V003   15 14 13 12

BIG IDEA Number Uses, Classification, and Representation Numbers can be used for different purposes, and numbers can be classified and represented in different ways.

ESSENTIAL UNDERSTANDINGS

11-1   There is more than one way to show a number.

11-2   The numbers 11, 12, and 13 can be decomposed as the sum of ten and some ones. The number 11 is decomposed to the sum of $10 + 1$, the number 12 is decomposed to $10 + 2$, and the number 13 is decomposed to $10 + 3$.

11-3   The numbers 14, 15, and 16 can be decomposed as the sum of ten and some ones. The number 14 is decomposed to $10 + 4$, the number 15 is decomposed to $10 + 5$, and the number 16 is decomposed to $10 + 6$.

11-4   The numbers 17, 18, and 19 can be decomposed as a ten and some ones. The number 17 is decomposed to $10 + 7$, the number 18 is decomposed to $10 + 8$, and the number 19 is decomposed to $10 + 9$.

BIG IDEA Practices, Processes, and Proficiencies Mathematics content and practices can be applied to solve problems.

ESSENTIAL UNDERSTANDING

11-5   Some problems can be solved by identifying elements that repeat in a predictable way.

How to Decompose Numbers 11 to 19

In Topic 11, children should become fluent with the use of double ten-frames. The use of double ten-frames is an efficient and intuitive way to model the decomposition of numbers 11 to 19 as a ten and some ones. For example, to decompose the number 17, children place 10 counters in one ten-frame and the remaining 7 counters in the other ten-frame. Instead of 17 randomly placed counters, the double ten-frame clearly organizes the counters as 1 ten and 7 ones. As children continue to practice with double ten-frames, they learn to link the model to its related addition number sentence.

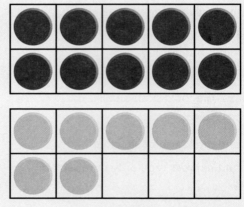

$$17 = 10 + 7$$

Place Value and Double Ten-Frames

The use of double ten-frames to decompose numbers 11 to 19 lays the foundation for children's understanding of place value. The ten-frame with 10 counters represents 1 ten, while the other ten-frame represents the number of ones.

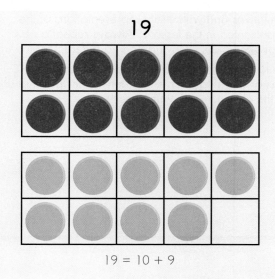

19

19 = 10 + 9

Mathematical Practices: Model with Mathematics

Encourage the use of red counters in one of the ten-frames and yellow counters in the other ten-frame. This emphasizes the concept of the numbers 11 to 19 as a ten and some ones.

Mathematical Practices: Use Appropriate Tools

Some children may decompose the numbers 11 to 19 in ways other than a ten and some ones. For example, a child may decompose 12 as $12 = 6 + 6$ instead of $12 = 10 + 2$. Although mathematically correct, $12 = 6 + 6$ does not emphasize that the number 12 can be expressed as 1 ten and 2 ones. The use of double ten-frames is a particularly effective way to help children express the numbers 11 to 19 as a ten and some ones.

For a complete list of *enVisionMATH* Professional Development resources in print, on DVD, and online, see the *Teacher's Program Overview*.

DIFFERENTIATED INSTRUCTION

 **INTERVENTION**

 **ELL** STRATEGY Strategies For All

ELL

Considerations for ELL Children

Some children may have difficulty differentiating between the spoken words *four* and *fourteen; six* and *sixteen; seven* and *seventeen; eight* and *eighteen;* and *nine* and *nineteen*. This may become particularly problematic in Topic 11, as they learn to decompose numbers 11 to 19 as a ten and some ones. Write the number pairs on the board before beginning the ELL strategies.

- Point to each 1-digit number as you say it; tap your shoe against the floor one time to stress that the word is monosyllabic. Then point to each 2-digit number as you say it; tap your shoe against the floor two times to stress that the word is disyllabic. Clearly pronounce the syllable *-teen* each time you say it. Be sure to explain that the numbers 7, 11, 12, and 17 are exceptions.

Special Needs RTI

Considerations for Special Needs Children

- Special needs children benefit from extra practice with manipulatives and with visual representations of the ideas presented in the lessons. Always repeat a new concept often before moving on to a different topic.

- If a child has difficulty coloring within specified regions or aligning counters on ten-frames evenly, allow the child to work with a partner.

Below Level RTI

Considerations for Below Level Children

- Some children may become discouraged if they easily lose track of how many counters they have placed in double ten-frames. For these children, you may wish to create numbered counters. You can do this by placing a number sticker or small square of masking tape (labeled 1 to 19) on each counter. Have children place these numbered counters in the double ten-frames in numeric order. Most children will quickly recognize that 5 counters always complete one row of a ten-frame, 10 counters always complete one full ten-frame, and that 15 counters always complete one full ten-frame and one row of a second ten-frame. Benchmarks such as these will help the child move toward using counters that are not numbered.

Advanced/Gifted

Considerations for Advanced/Gifted Children

- Show advanced and gifted children that addends may change places without changing the sum. For example, display double ten-frames that model $15 = 10 + 5$. Switch the placement of the counters in the top ten-frames to illustrate that 15 is also equal to $5 + 10$. Encourage children to apply the Commutative Property of Addition to other addition number sentences.

Response to Intervention

 RTI TIER **1** ONGOING

Ongoing Intervention
- Lessons with guiding questions to assess understanding
- Support to prevent misconceptions and to reteach

 RTI TIER **2** STRATEGIC

Strategic Intervention
- Targeted to small groups who need more support
- Easy to implement

 RTI TIER **3** INTENSIVE

Intensive Intervention
- Instruction to accelerate progress
- Instruction focused on foundational skills

MATHEMATICAL
PRACTICES

Reading Comprehension and Problem Solving

ⓒ **Use Structure:**

Using Reading Comprehension Strategies

Even when math problems are presented using a picture book format, a good reading comprehension strategy to use in math problem solving is to use prior knowledge to look for patterns in pictures and number sentences.

Questions to Guide Comprehension

Use these questions with Lesson 11-5, Guided Practice. *What do you need to find out?* [How to model the number 12 with counters and how to write an addition number sentence to match the model] *What do you know?* [I can use a double ten-frame to show the number 12. This can help me write the matching addition number sentence.] *What do you do first?* [I draw 10 counters in the first ten-frame and 2 in the second ten-frame to show the number 12.] *What do you do next?* [I write the addition 12 = 10 + 2 to match the drawing.]

Act It Out! *How can you use counters to solve the problem?* Have children use counters in ten-frames to show the number 12.

Talk It Out! *How can you tell a story while you act it out?* Have children tell a story about a set of 10 animals and a set of 2 animals going to the park as children place 12 counters in the ten-frames.

Draw It Out! *How can you draw a picture to solve the problem?* Have children use yellow and red crayons to show the number 12 as 10 red counters and 2 yellow counters in the ten-frames.

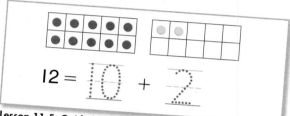

Lesson 11-5, Guided Practice

Vocabulary Activities

Ready, *Set*, Go!

ⓒ **Attend to Precision** To prepare for this activity, write several different sets of numbers on index cards, such as "set of 4" or "set of 6". Be sure that the total sum of all the sets is equal to the total number of children in your classroom.

Review the meaning of the word *set* with children. Randomly distribute the index cards to volunteers as you recd the words on the cards aloud. Explain that when you say *Go!* children should stand up and form "sets of children" to match the sets on the cards. Then say: *Ready, set, go!* After they form "sets of children" next to each index card, have children in each group say, "We are a set of [4]," as they show the index card to the class.

set of 4

set of 6

Math Center

Frame Game

Materials
(per class) masking tape

- With masking tape, create 2 very large ten-frames on the classroom floor. They should be large enough for children to stand in.

- Say the number 14. Have 10 children stand in one ten-frame and 4 children stand in the other. Ask children to name the addition number sentence that matches the ten-frames. [14 = 10 + 4]

- Depending on the number of children in your classroom, repeat the activity with other numbers from 11 to 19.

Writing Center

Break Apart the Cubes

Materials
(per child) 19 connecting cubes, writing paper

- Have each child connect 19 cubes together to make a very long rod. Have them count aloud to 19 as they connect the cubes.

- Tell children to break apart the rod to make 2 separate rods. Explain that one rod must have exactly 10 cubes in it.

- Have children count the number of cubes in the other rod. [9]

- Children then write the number sentence 19 = 10 + 9 to match how they broke apart their rods.

- Repeat the activity with 12 connecting cubes.

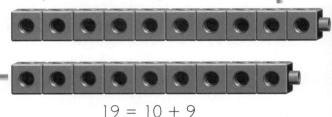

19 = 10 + 9

Dramatic Play Center

Muffins for Sale!

Materials
(per class) 2 paper plates, 19 counters

- Invite volunteers to stand in front of the class to be "bakers." Explain that they just baked 15 muffins. Give 15 counters to the bakers and explain that each counter stands for 1 muffin. Encourage the bakers to pretend the counters are real muffins by smelling and touching them.

- Give the bakers 2 plates. Explain that the bakers will sell 10 of their muffins and keep the other muffins to take home.

- Ask children how many of the 15 muffins should go on the plate to sell. [10]. Then ask how many muffins should go on the plate for the bakers to take home. [5] Have the bakers place the counters on each plate as you write the number sentence on the board: 15 = 10 + 5.

- Repeat the activity with other volunteers and different numbers of muffins (from 11 to 19 muffins in all).

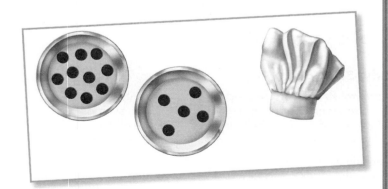

Art Center

Bears in Two Caves

Materials
(per child) 2 index cards, brown crayon, writing paper

- Give 1 index card to each child and explain that it is a "bear cave."
- Tell children that 18 bears are looking for a cave to sleep in, but only 10 bears can fit in this cave. Have children draw 10 bears on each of their index cards, or "caves."
- When each index card has 10 bears drawn on it, give children another index card, or "cave." Explain that the other bears can sleep in this cave. Elicit how many bears are still looking for a cave. [8 bears]
- When children have finished coloring the 8 bears on the index cards, guide children to see that the addition sentence that matches their pictures is 18 = 10 + 8.

Movement Center

Find Your Partner

Materials
Index cards

- On index cards, write addition number sentences that show how to decompose numbers 11 to 19: 11 = 10 + 1, 12 = 10 + 2, 13 = 10 + 3, etc. On separate index cards, draw double ten-frames and counters that match each addition number sentence you wrote.
- Shuffle and distribute all the cards to children. Instruct each child to find his or her partner with the matching number sentence or model.
- When all cards have been matched, you can collect, shuffle, and redistribute the index cards for additional practice.

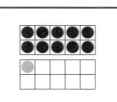

$$11 = 10 + 1$$

On the Ice

This is a story in which children write number sentences to show teen numbers as sums of ten and some more.

This book belongs to:

Avi

On the Ice

Do you like the ice? These animals like to play on the ice!

Topic 11   1

10 penguins play on the ice.
Then __2__ more penguins come.
Now there are __12__ penguins.
10 + __2__ = __12__

Topic 11   2

---

1 ▸ **Before the Story**

Picture Walk

Ask children to look at the pages. *What kinds of animals are in the story?* [Penguins, bears, seals] *Do you think this story takes place somewhere where it is warm, or somewhere where it is cold? Why?* [Cold; they are cold-weather animals wearing winter clothing]

Activate Prior Knowledge

In this story, we will be joining two groups of animals. The first group will have 10 animals. Then some more animals will come to join them. Let's practice putting 10 together with some extras. Draw a ten-frame on the board and fill it with circles. Draw three more circles to the right of the ten-frame. *I see 10 circles and 3 more circles. How many circles in all?* Write the number sentence $10 + 3 = 13$ on the board and read it with children. *10 and 3 is 13. There are 13 in all. $13 = 10 + 3$*

2 ▸ **During the Story**

READ

Read the story aloud for enjoyment. Then read each page aloud and wait for children to respond to the text. Have children identify how many animals there are in each group. Encourage them to determine how many there are in all. Then have them say the number sentence that shows the whole equals the sum of the parts (e.g., $15 = 10 + 5$).

GESTURE

Have 10 children stand up to represent the original group of penguins. *How many more penguins come?* [2] Have 2 more children come up to represent those penguins. *Here is a group of...* [10] *And here is a group of...* [2] *Point to the group of 10. Point to the group of 2.* Repeat as needed for the polar bears and seals.

0 polar bears play
on the ice.

Then __4__ more polar
bears come.

Now there are __14__
polar bears.

10 + __4__ = __14__

Topic 11 **3**

10 seals play on the ice.

Then __5__ more seals
come.

Now there are __15__
seals.

10 + __5__ = __15__

Topic 11 **4**

fold down

3 > After the Story

Extension

On chart paper, write a new "On the Ice" page with children. Have them choose a new kind of animal (which does not need to be an animal that commonly lives on the ice). Have them draw simple pictures that show 10 of these animals playing on the ice, and circle the group of 10. Then have them choose how many more of the animals (up to 9) will come to join the original group of 10. Have children draw these animals as well and write the number sentence that shows how many in all. Read the page aloud with children and post it where it is easy to see.

You may wish to have children take home their Interactive Math Story and share what they have learned about writing number sentences to show teen numbers.

COLOR

Distribute the Interactive Math Story to children. Explain that the animals in the story live in icy places, where there are not many colors, and that the animals are mostly black, white, and gray. Have children color all the penguins black, color all the seals gray, and leave all the polar bears white.

WRITE

On pages 2–4, have children circle each group of 10 animals. Then have them count and write how many new animals there are and how many there are in all. Finally, have them complete the number sentence. Remind them to use what they know about teen numbers to help them.

SPEAK

Ask children to retell the story in their own words. For each page, have volunteers explain how they knew how many animals there were in all. Have children share the number sentences that they wrote to match the pictures.

Name _____

DOMAIN Number and Operations in Base Ten

Topic
11

Decomposing Numbers 11 to 19

Review What You Know

①

18

②

$2 + 3 = 5$

③

$10 + 6 = 16$

Directions Have children: **1.** count the counters and write the number that tells how many; **2.** count the objects in each group and write the correct numbers on the lines to complete the addition sentence; **3.** count the counters and write the numbers that complete the number sentence.

© Pearson Education, Inc. K

Home-School Connection

Dear Family,

Today my class started Topic 11, **Decomposing Numbers 11 to 19.** I will learn to break the numbers 11 to 19 into parts made up of ten ones and some further ones. I will also write number sentences to show how I broke the numbers into parts. Here are some of the new math words I will be learning and some things we can do to help me with my math.

Love, _____

Book to Read

Reading math stories reinforces concepts. Look for this title in your local library:

12 Ways to Get to 11 by Eve Merriam (Aladdin Paperbacks, 1993)

Home Activity

Draw two 5 × 2 grids (ten-frames) on paper as shown in the photo. Have your child count handfuls of 11–19 objects, such as peas, beans, or paper clips, by placing one in each square of the first grid and then continuing with the second grid.

My New Math Words

double ten-frame

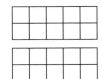

set

Review What You Know

Purpose

Diagnose children's readiness by assessing prerequisite content. Assign each set of exercises and go over the answers with children.

Understanding by Design

Children will be able to answer the Topic Essential Question by the end of the topic. Revisit the question throughout the topic. Then use the Topic 11 Performance Assessment.

Topic Essential Question

• How can we break the numbers 11–19 into parts?

"Understanding by Design" is registered as a trademark with the Patent and Trademark Office by the Association for Supervision of Curriculum Development (ASCD). ASCD has not authorized, approved or sponsored this work and is in no way affiliated with Pearson or its products.

set

Cards can always be used as flash cards. Have children create large vocabulary cards with visuals to add to the classroom word wall.

Take Home the Bears

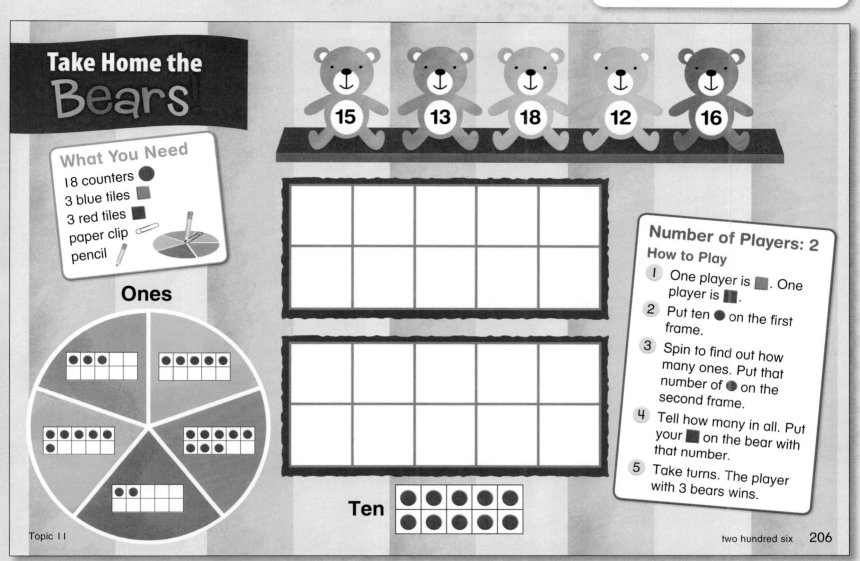

What You Need

- 18 counters ●
- 3 blue tiles ■
- 3 red tiles ■
- paper clip
- pencil

Ones

Ten

Number of Players: 2

How to Play

1. One player is ■. One player is ■.
2. Put ten ● on the first frame.
3. Spin to find out how many ones. Put that number of ● on the second frame.
4. Tell how many in all. Put your ■ on the bear with that number.
5. Take turns. The player with 3 bears wins.

15 13 18 12 16

Game
for school or home

Purpose

Provide children with an opportunity to practice prerequisite skills. You may wish to remind children that on each turn they should place a counter in each square of the top ten-frame and then add counters to the bottom ten-frame to match the spinner.

Demonstrate writing a number to match what is shown in the ten-frames: *I write a 1 to stand for the ten and a 3 to stand for the three ones. The number is 13.*

Math Project

Art

Directions

Assign each child a different number between 11 and 19. Have each child use strips of construction paper to make a paper chain with the assigned number of links. For example, the child assigned 15 will use 15 loops of construction paper to make his or her chain.

Hang the chains in order from the ceiling or another high place. Attach a sign to the bottom of each chain displaying the number the chain represents.

C
Common Core

Domain

Number and Operations in Base Ten

Cluster

Work with numbers 11–19 to gain foundations for place value.

Standard

K.NBT.1 Compose and decompose numbers from 11 to 19 into ten ones and some further ones, e.g., by using objects or drawings, and record each composition or decomposition by a drawing or equation (e.g., 18 = 10 + 8); understand that these numbers are composed of ten ones and one, two, three, four, five, six, seven, eight, or nine ones.

Mathematical Practices

- ✔ Make sense of problems and persevere in solving them.
- ✔ Reason abstractly and quantitatively.
- ○ Construct viable arguments and critique the reasoning of others.
- ✔ Model with mathematics.
- ✔ Use appropriate tools strategically.
- ✔ Attend to precision.
- ✔ Look for and make use of structure.
- ○ Look for and express regularity in repeated reasoning.

Creating Sets to 19

 **Lesson Overview**

Objective	Essential Understanding	Vocabulary	Materials
Children will use objects to create sets to 19.	There is more than one way to show a number.	**double ten-frame set**	Number Cards 11–19 (Teaching Tools 5, 6), counters (or Teaching Tool 32), glue

C PROFESSIONAL DEVELOPMENT

Math Background

Children begin to visualize the relationship between ten and the teen numbers by using ten-frames. Using ten-frames helps them visualize that a teen number is 10 and some more. Children will begin to develop an understanding of place-value and two-digit numbers.

1 Daily Common Core Review

Daily Common Core Review

Name _____

Daily Common Core Review 11-1

🌟

Ⓐ (desks)

Ⓑ (desks)

● (desks)

Ⓓ (desks)

❷ (building)

● Ⓐ 0

Ⓑ 1

Ⓒ 2

Ⓓ 10

Directions Have students mark the best answer. 🌟 Which picture shows 7 desks? ❷ Which tells the number of apples that are in the basket?

11-1

Content Reviewed

Exercise 1   Count and Recognize a Number of Objects

Exercise 2   Use Numbers to Tell How Many

Also available in print

 MATHEMATICAL PRACTICES

 30 min

Problem-Based Interactive Learning

Overview Children will learn to create sets of objects up to 19 by counting on from 10 and by adding a number to 10.

Focus What strategies can you use to find the number of objects in a set greater than 10?

Materials (per child) Number Cards 11–19 (Teaching Tools 5, 6), counters (or Teaching Tool 32), glue

Vocabulary set, double ten-frame

Set the Purpose Remind children that they have learned how to find the number of objects in a set. *You will use counters and ten-frames to help you find numbers greater than 10 in different ways in this lesson.*

Connect Hold up both of your hands with all of your fingers extended. *How many fingers am I holding up?* [10] Ask a child to stand next to you and extend 9 fingers. *How many fingers are we holding up in all?* [19]

MATHEMATICAL PRACTICES

Use Appropriate Tools
Ask children how using a double ten-frame helps them count the objects.

Academic Vocabulary *A group of objects that belong together can be called a* **set**. Draw a ten-frame and a **double ten-frame** on the board. *You have learned to use ten-frames to show numbers. A double-ten frame is like a ten-frame. It is used to show numbers greater than 10.*

Pose the Problem *Hannah wants to make a set of 17. How can she make a set of 17 counters?* Have children share their ideas.

Model Hold up the number card for 17 and then place it in the box next to the double ten-frame. Place 10 counters in the top ten-frame and have children do the same. *How many counters are there?* [10] *How do you know?* [The ten-frame is filled.] Place 7 counters in the bottom ten-frame and have children do the same. *How many counters did you place in the bottom ten-frame?* [7] *How many counters are there in all?* [17] *How do you know that your set shows 17?* [Possible responses: I counted them; I made 10, then counted 11, 12, 13, 14, 15, 16, 17; I filled up 1 ten-frame and then added 7 more counters.] *Remember what we learned about number sentences. How can we write the set of 17 as a number sentence using the number 10?* [10 and 7 is 17.] *What numbers would we write if we counted on from 10 to 17?* [11, 12, 13, 14, 15, 16, 17] Encourage children to use 10 as a benchmark by either saying a number sentence or counting on from 10. Have children repeat the process for the number 18.

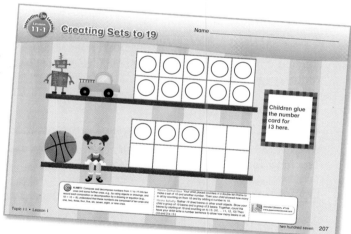

Small-Group Interaction *Show me 13 counters. How do you know there are 13?* [Possible response: I made 10, then counted 11, 12, 13.] Have children glue the number card for 13 in the box and draw 13 counters in the double ten-frame.

You have 13 counters on your workmat. Show me how you can make a set of 18 from your set of 13. How did you make 18? [Possible responses: by adding 5; by counting on from 13]

 eTools **Counters**
www.pearsonsuccessnet.com

3 Develop the Concept: Visual

Visual Learning

What number is on the card? [12] *How can you make 12 by using ten-frames?* [Have children share their ideas.]

How many counters did Hannah put in the top ten-frame? [10] *In the bottom ten-frame?* [2] *What did Hannah do next?* [Added 10 and 2] *What does her addition sentence show?* [10 + 2 = 12] *So how many counters are there in all?* [12 counters]

10 and 2 is 12.

1 Visual Learning

Set the Purpose Call children's attention to the **Visual Learning Bridge** at the top of the page. *In this lesson, you will use objects to create sets to 19.*

 Animated Glossary Children can see highlighted words defined in the Online Student Edition.
double ten-frame, set
www.pearsonsuccessnet.com

2 Guided Practice

Remind children to look at the counters and ten-frames at the top of the page to help them.

Error Intervention

If children have difficulty drawing the correct number of counters,

then have them work with counters and a double ten-frame (or Teaching Tool 9).

Do you understand? *How many counters did you draw in the top ten-frame?* [10] *How many counters did you draw in the bottom ten-frame?* [Answers will vary.] *How many counters did you draw in all?* [Answers will vary.]

Reteaching Have children use objects such as crayons or paper clips to first make a set of 10 and then count on or add a number of objects 1 through 9 to the set of 10. Repeat with many different numbers.

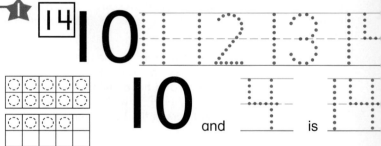

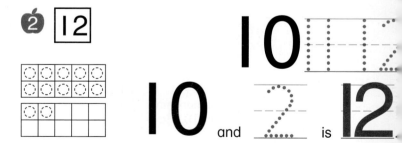

Directions Have children draw counters in the double ten-frame to show the number on each number card. Then have them show the number on the number card by counting on from 10 and completing the number sentence.

Topic 11 • Lesson 1

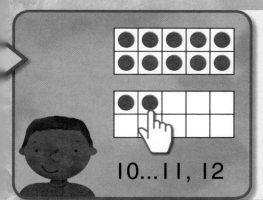

How many counters did Marty put in the top ten-frame? [10] *In the bottom ten-frame?* [2] *What did Marty do next?* [He started with 10 and counted on.] *How many counters are there in all?* [12]

Did Hannah and Marty count every counter to find how many in all? [No] *What did Hannah do?* [Added] *What did Marty do?* [Counted on] *Why did they get the same answer?* [There are different ways to make the same set.]

Additional Activity

Sets of Objects

⏱ 10 min 👥

Materials (per pair) Double ten-frames (Teaching Tool 9), Writing Practice (Teaching Tool 15), 19 small objects: beads or buttons

- Have children count out a group of 10 beads and a group of 7 beads.
- Have them place the beads in their double ten-frames. Then have them count the beads aloud beginning with 10 and counting 10, …11, 12, 13, 14, 15, 16, 17.
- Then have children write a number sentence to show how many beads they have in all. [10 and 7 is 17.]
- Repeat with other sets of objects if you wish.

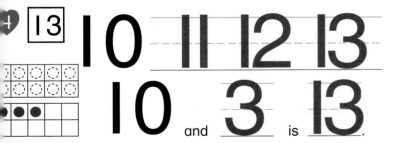

15 10 11 12 13 14 15

10 and ____ 5 is 15.

13 10 11 12 13

10 and ____ 3 is 13.

Directions Have children draw counters in the double ten-frame to show the number on each number card. Then have them show the number on the number card by counting on from 10 and completing the number sentence.

two hundred eight   208

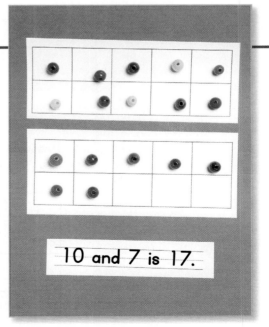

10 and 7 is 17.

---

3 Independent Practice

Have children draw counters in the double ten-frame to show the number on each number card. Then have them show the number by counting on from 10 and by adding a number to 10.

208A

Close

Essential Understanding There is more than one way to show a number. *You can use objects to create sets to 19.*

 ASSESSMENT

Exercise 1 is worth 1 point.

Use the rubric to score Exercise 2.

Exercise 2

Model with Mathematics Children should be able to correctly draw the counters in the double ten-frame to show the number on the number card and then count on from 10 to show how many counters in all.

ELL Use Repetition For children who need additional help following directions, have them repeat key words and phrases before beginning their work.

Student Samples
3-point answer Children draw 7 more counters and count on to 17 correctly.

2-point answer Children draw 7 more counters but do not count on to 17 correctly.

1-point answer Children do not draw 7 more counters and do not count on correctly.

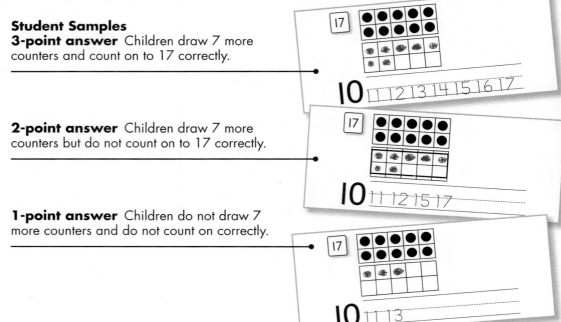

Quick Check Master

Name _____

Quick Check 11-1

Ⓐ 10 and 5 is 15.
Ⓑ 10 and 6 is 16.
Ⓒ 8 and 8 is 16.
Ⓓ 10 and 8 is 18.

17

10 _____

See student samples at the right.

 **Formative** Assessment

Use the **Quick Check** to assess children's understanding.

Prescription for Differentiated Instruction
Use children's work on the **Quick Check** to prescribe differentiated instruction.

Points	Prescription
0–2	Intervention
3	On-Level
4	Advanced

Differentiated Instruction

Intervention

Number Sentences

  10 min

Materials Counters (or Teaching Tool 32), double ten-frame (or Teaching Tool 9)

• Have children model numbers 11–19 using counters on their double ten-frames.

• For each number, have children repeat and complete this sentence: *10 and _____ is _____.* [Answers will vary.]

On-Level

Practice | **Center Activity**

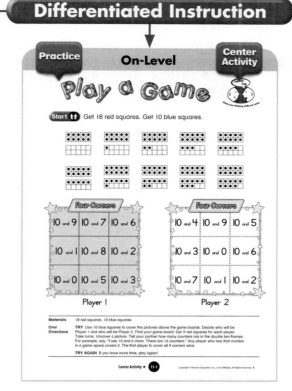

Advanced

Practice | **Center Activity**

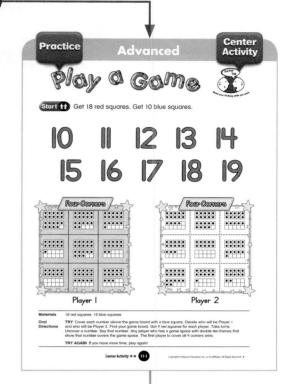

ELL Report Back To check understanding, ask a child to repeat and complete this sentence: *If every space is filled on one ten-frame and the next ten-frame has 3 spaces filled, the number in all is _____.* [Thirteen]

Leveled Homework

Reteaching Master

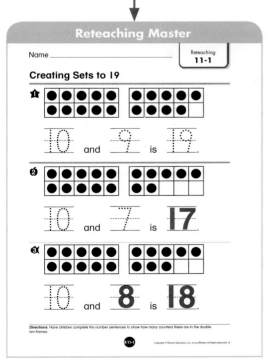

Also available in print

eTools **Counters**
www.pearsonsuccessnet.com

Practice Master

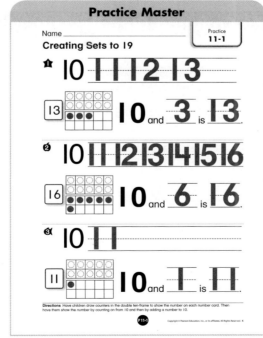

Also available in print

eTools **Counters**
www.pearsonsuccessnet.com

Enrichment Master

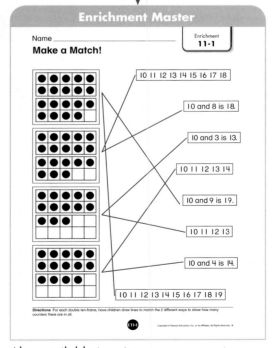

Also available in print

eTools **Counters**
www.pearsonsuccessnet.com

Parts of 11, 12, and 13

Common Core

Domain
Number and Operations in Base Ten

Cluster
Work with numbers 11–19 to gain foundations for place value.

Standard
K.NBT.1 Compose and decompose numbers from 11 to 19 into ten ones and some further ones, e.g., by using objects or drawings, and record each composition or decomposition by a drawing or equation (e.g., 18 = 10 + 8); understand that these numbers are composed of ten ones and one, two, three, four, five, six, seven, eight, or nine ones.

Mathematical Practices
○ Make sense of problems and persevere in solving them.

☑ Reason abstractly and quantitatively.

○ Construct viable arguments and critique the reasoning of others.

☑ Model with mathematics.

☑ Use appropriate tools strategically.

○ Attend to precision.

○ Look for and make use of structure.

☑ Look for and express regularity in repeated reasoning.

Quick and Easy Lesson Overview

Objective	Essential Understanding	Vocabulary	Materials
Children will represent the decomposition of 11, 12, and 13 as ten ones and additional ones.	The numbers 11, 12, and 13 can be decomposed as the sum of ten and some ones. The number 11 is decomposed to $10 + 1$, the number 12 is decomposed to $10 + 2$, and the number 13 is decomposed to $10 + 3$.		Counters (or Teaching Tool 32)

Ⓒ **PROFESSIONAL DEVELOPMENT**

Math Background

Decomposition of numbers is helpful in developing a child's number sense. The concept will later be applied to the standard algorithms for addition and subtraction. The decomposition of a teen number into the parts of ten and some more is a beginning foundation to later work with larger numbers.

For example, if a child wanted to add $18 + 15$, he or she could simply decompose the numbers into $10 + 8$ and $10 + 5$. If a child can decompose numbers into tens and ones, they can better understand quantitative relationships and flexibly use numbers and operations to solve problems.

1 Daily Common Core Review

Daily Common Core Review

Name _____

Daily Common Core Review **11-2**

❶
Ⓐ
Ⓑ
Ⓒ
Ⓓ

❷
Ⓐ
Ⓑ
Ⓒ
●

❸
Ⓐ 30   Ⓒ 10
Ⓑ 20   Ⓓ 5

Directions Have children: ★ fill in the bubble next to the picture that matches the number of shaded parts; ◆ fill in the bubble next to the group that shows 2 fewer counters; ■ fill in the bubble next to the number of cubes shown.

11-2

Copyright © Pearson Education, Inc., or its affiliates. All Rights Reserved.

Content Reviewed

Exercise 1   Find 2 Equal Sets

Exercise 2   Identify 2 Fewer

Exercise 3   Counting Groups of 10

Also available in print

 30 min # Problem-Based Interactive Learning

Overview Children will make drawings and write equations that represent the decomposition of 11, 12, and 13 as ten ones and some additional ones.

Focus How can 11, 12, and 13 be broken apart into ten ones and some more ones using a drawing and a number sentence?

Materials Counters (or Teaching Tool 32)

 **Engage**

Set the Purpose *You have learned how to make the numbers 11 to 19 using ten-frames. Today, you will learn how to begin with 11, 12, or 13 and then break it into two parts, with one part being ten.*

Connect Ask a child to stand up and display all 10 of his or her fingers. Ask a second child to hold up 2 more fingers. *How many fingers are showing in all?* [12] *How many fingers are in the first group?* [10] *How many more fingers are in the second group?* [2] Together as a class, count to make sure the groups total 12.

 **MATHEMATICAL PRACTICES**

Reason Abstractly
Remind children that the ten-frame with 10 counters represents ten ones, or one ten, and the counters in the second ten-frame represent the additional ones. Numbers 11, 12, and 13 can be broken into ten and one, two, or three ones.

Pose the Problem *There are 13 children waiting in line for a train ride. There are only 10 seats in each train car. If the conductor fills up one car with 10 children, how many will be left to ride in the second car?* [Have children share ideas before modeling the situation.]

Model *Let's use counters to show 13 children on the double ten-frame.* Place 10 counters in the top ten-frame and have children do the same. *How many counters are showing?* [10] *Ten children are on the first train car.* Place 3 counters on the bottom ten-frame and have children do the same. *How many counters are in the bottom ten-frame?* [3] *How many counters are there in all?* [13] Draw children's attention to the 13 in the bottom number sentence on their page. *What does this number represent?* [The number of children in all] *How many children were in the first group?* [10] Have children trace the 10 in the number sentence at the bottom of the workmat. *How many children were in the second group?* [3] Direct children to write the number 3 to complete the number sentence. *How do you know that your double ten-frame shows 13?* [We can count to check.]

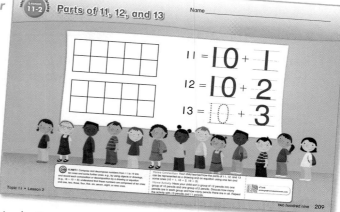

Small-Group Interaction Have pairs of children work together to fill in the ten-frames and write the number sentences for 11 and 12. First, they should model it with counters on the double ten-frame and then write the number sentence. Facilitate their work by asking questions. *Suppose I have 11 counters. If I fill up one ten-frame with counters, how many will be left to put in the second ten-frame? Why did you completely fill the first ten-frame? How does your number sentence tell about your counters?* Guide children to see how the number sentences relate to 11, 12, and 13 as combinations of ten ones and one, two, or three additional ones.

 Extend

How could you break apart 14 into ten ones and some more ones using a double ten-frame and counters? What number sentence would you write? [Allow children to share ideas.]

 eTools **Counters**
www.pearsonsuccessnet.com

Visual Learning

The Dolphin Swim Team won 13 trophies. How could they split the trophies into two groups to put on two trophy cases? [Have children share their ideas.]

How many trophies are there in all? [13] *How many trophies are in the red case?* [10] *How many trophies are in the yellow case?* [3]

1 Visual Learning

Set the Purpose Call children's attention to the Visual Learning Bridge at the top of the page. *In this lesson, you will learn to show 11, 12, and 13 as two parts, with ten ones as one part.*

2 Guided Practice

Remind children to break apart numbers 11 to 13 into a group of 10 ones, or one ten, and a group of one, two, or three extra ones.

Exercise 1
Error Intervention

If children do not make a group of 10 counters,

then remind them to fill up one ten-frame entirely with 10 counters before moving on to the other ten-frame.

Do you understand? *How can you use ten-frames to help you write 13 as two parts with 10 as one part?* [Count out the number of counters in all. Fill a ten-frame with 10 counters. Then use the extra counters to fill the new ten-frame. The number sentence is 10 + the number of counters in the second ten-frame.]

Reteaching Display 12 counters. From those 12 counters, ask children to separate a group of 10 counters. *There are 10 ones in this group. We can call this group one ten. How many more counters are there?* [2] Write 12 = 10 + 2 on the board. Review with children how the number sentence relates to 12 as a combination of 10 ones and 2 more ones. Repeat the process with 11 and 13.

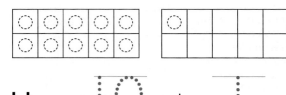

1

$$11 = 10 + 1$$

2

$$12 = 10 + 2$$

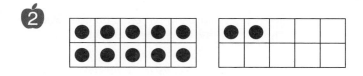

Directions Have children: **1.** count out 11 counters, trace them in the ten-frames, and trace the number sentence to match the drawings in the ten-frames; **2.** count out 12 counters, draw them in the ten-frames, and write a number sentence to match the drawings in the ten-frames.

Topic 11 • Lesson 2

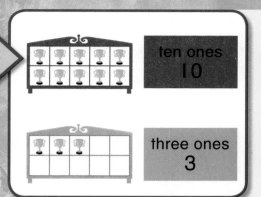

What does the phrase "ten ones" and the number 10 represent in the red box? [The 10 trophies in the red trophy case] *What does "three ones" and the number 3 represent in the yellow box?* [The 3 extra trophies]

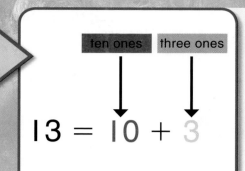

Read the number sentence with me: 13 equals 10 plus 3. What does the 10 represent? [The group of 10 trophies; 10 ones] *What does the 3 represent?* [The group of 3 trophies; 3 ones] *Which number tells the total number of trophies?* [13]

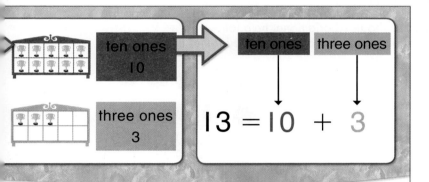

③

$$13 = 10 + 3$$

④

$$11 = 10 + 1$$

Directions Have children: **3.** count out 13 counters, draw them in the ten-frames, and write a number sentence to match the drawings in the ten-frames; **4.** count out 11 counters, draw them in the ten-frames, and write a number sentence to match the drawings in the ten-frames.

two hundred ten   210

Number Sculptures

🕐 10–15 min   👫

Materials (per pair) 13 craft sticks, two balls of clay

- Have children count out 11 craft sticks.
- Then have children make a sculpture by putting 10 sticks into one ball of clay. Then have them put the remaining stick into the other ball of clay. Have children write a number sentence to represent the sticks in their sculpture.
- Repeat for 12 sticks and 13 sticks.

---

3   Independent Practice

Children decompose numbers 11 to 13 into two groups. The first group is ten ones and the second is one, two, or three more ones.

4 Close/Assess and Differentiate

Close

Essential Understanding There is more than one way to show a number. The numbers 11, 12, and 13 can be broken up into one ten and one, two, or three more ones. *You can show the numbers 11, 12, and 13 in two parts where one part is 10.*

 ASSESSMENT

Exercise 1 is worth 1 point.
Use the rubric to score Exercise 2.

Exercise 2

Use Appropriate Tools Children should be able to draw two new counters in the top ten-frame and cross out two counters in the bottom ten-frame to match the number sentence.

ELL Rephrase For children who need additional help following directions, rephrase a question or statement in a different way rather than repeating it.

Student Samples
3-point answer Children correctly draw 2 counters in the first ten-frame and cross out 2 counters in the second ten-frame. The double ten-frame matches the number sentence.

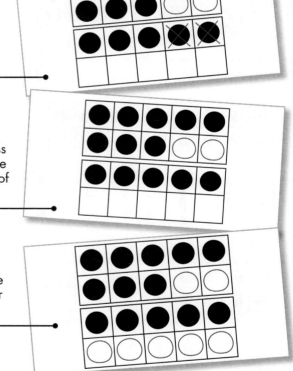

2-point answer Children draw 2 more counters in the first ten-frame but do not cross out any counters in the second ten-frame. The double ten-frame does not match each part of the number sentence.

1-point answer Children do not draw or cross out the correct number of counters. The double ten-frame does not match the number sentence.

Quick Check Master

Name_____ Quick Check **11-2**

Ⓐ 11 = 5 + 6 Ⓒ 12 = 6 + 6
Ⓑ 11 = 10 + 1 Ⓓ 12 = 10 + 2

13 = 10 + 3

See student samples at the right.

Directions Have children: ⓐ fill in the bubble next to the number sentence that tells about the double ten-frame; ⓑ correct the double ten-frame to match the number sentence by marking Xs on counters in the wrong place and drawing new counters in the correct place.

Formative Assessment

Use the **Quick Check** to assess children's understanding.

Prescription for Differentiated Instruction

Use children's work on the **Quick Check** to prescribe differentiated instruction.

Points	Prescription
0–2	**Intervention**
3	**On-Level**
4	**Advanced**

210B Topic 11

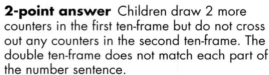

Differentiated Instruction

Intervention

Different Items

 10–15 min

Materials 13 paper clips

- Have children count out 11 paper clips.
- Have children experiment with making two groups of the paper clips. As they form each group, have them count the number of paper clips in each group. Then have them confirm there are still 11 paper clips.
- Then have children count out 10 paper clips and confirm there is 1 paper clip left over in the other group. Discuss how this is like a ten-frame.
- Repeat for 12 paper clips and 13 paper clips.

Practice · On-Level · Center Activity

Look and See

Start Get 18 red squares. Get [dice].

Materials 18 red squares, 3 number cubes

Oral Directions **TRY** Take turns. Toss 3 number cubes. Count the dots. Say the number in all. Pretend your squares are fish. Show that number of fish in the fish tanks at the bottom of the page. Tell your partner if there are more fish in the tanks at the bottom of the page or in the tanks at the top of the page. Remove the squares. Take turns until each player has 5 turns.

TRY AGAIN If you have more time, play again!

Center Activity ★ 11-2   Copyright © Pearson Education, Inc., or its affiliates. All Rights Reserved.

Practice · Advanced · Center Activity

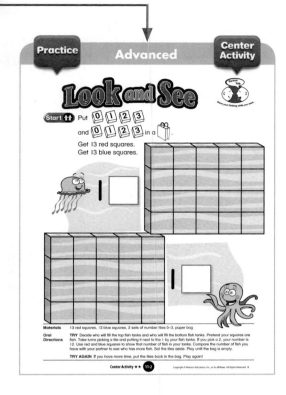

Look and See

Start Put [0 1 2 3] and [0 1 2 3] in a [bag]. Get 13 red squares. Get 13 blue squares.

Materials 13 red squares, 13 blue squares, 2 sets of number tiles 0–3, paper bag

Oral Directions **TRY** Decide who will fill the top fish tanks and who will fill the bottom fish tanks. Pretend your squares are fish. Take turns picking a tile and putting it next to the 1 by your fish tanks. If you pick 2, your number is 12. Use red and blue squares to show that number of fish in your tanks. Compare the number of fish you have with your partner to see who has more fish. Set the tiles aside. Play until the bag is empty.

TRY AGAIN If you have more time, put the tiles back in the bag. Play again!

Center Activity ★★ 11-2   Copyright © Pearson Education, Inc., or its affiliates. All Rights Reserved.

ELL Partner Talk Listen for conversations that describe different arrangements of the same number. For example, a child might say, "Here is the same number of squares in a different way."

Leveled Homework

Reteaching Master

Name _____
Parts of 11, 12, and 13   Reteaching 11-2

① $12 = 10 + 2$

② $11 = 10 + 1$

③ $13 = 10 + 3$

Directions Have children look at the groups of ten-frames and complete the number sentences

Also available in print

Practice Master

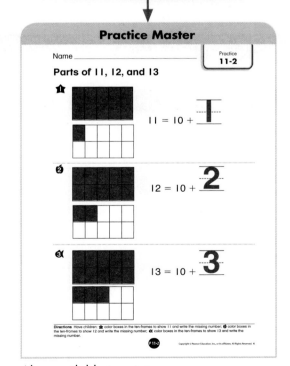

Name _____
Parts of 11, 12, and 13   Practice 11-2

① $11 = 10 + 1$

② $12 = 10 + 2$

③ $13 = 10 + 3$

Directions Have children: ① color boxes in the ten-frames to show 11 and write the missing number; ② color boxes in the ten-frames to show 12 and write the missing number; ③ color boxes in the ten-frames to show 13 and write the missing number.

Also available in print

Enrichment Master

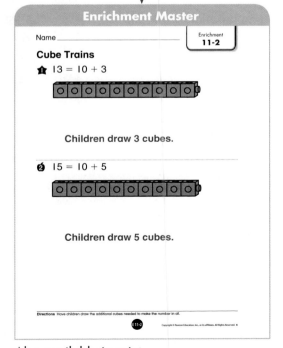

Name _____
       Enrichment 11-2

Cube Trains

① $13 = 10 + 3$

Children draw 3 cubes.

② $15 = 10 + 5$

Children draw 5 cubes.

Directions Have children draw the additional cubes needed to make the number in all.

Also available in print

Parts of 14, 15, and 16

Domain
Number and Operations in Base Ten

Cluster
Work with numbers 11–19 to gain foundations for place value.

Standard
K.NBT.1 Compose and decompose numbers from 11 to 19 into ten ones and some further ones, e.g., by using objects or drawings, and record each composition or decomposition by a drawing or equation (e.g., 18 = 10 + 8); understand that these numbers are composed of ten ones and one, two, three, four, five, six, seven, eight, or nine ones.

Mathematical Practices

✔ Make sense of problems and persevere in solving them.

✔ Reason abstractly and quantitatively.

✔ Construct viable arguments and critique the reasoning of others.

✔ Model with mathematics.

○ Use appropriate tools strategically.

✔ Attend to precision.

○ Look for and make use of structure.

✔ Look for and express regularity in repeated reasoning.

Lesson Overview

Objective	Essential Understanding	Vocabulary	Materials
Children will represent the decomposition of 14, 15, and 16 as one ten and four, five, or six ones.	Teen numbers can be decomposed as the sum of ten and some ones. The number 14 is decomposed to 10 + 4, the number 15 is decomposed to 10 + 5, and the number 16 is decomposed to 10 + 6.		Counters (or Teaching Tool 32)

PROFESSIONAL DEVELOPMENT

Math Background

When children write equations, they are forming an abstract sentence that can apply to a limitless number of situations. For children to use this mathematical power, they must be able to take situations and problems from their world and connect them to symbols and numbers in mathematical terms. That process is called *mathematizing*. To *mathematize* situations, young children must have many experiences and guidance, learn to write formal mathematical notation (e.g., = and +), and use these symbols to describe a drawing that represents the situation (NRC, 2009).

Please note that in this lesson, children begin by contextualizing the children on train cars that only hold 10, they then progress to using faces as they might appear on a bus, then they use more abstract counters, and finally they use numerals and symbols to describe how many. They then are required to decontextualize the situation by responding to questions about the meaning of each of the symbols involved. To reason abstractly and quantitatively, young children must develop both the ability to decontextualize and contextualize.

1 Daily Common Core Review

Daily Common Core Review

Name _____

Daily Common Core Review
11-3

1. Ⓐ ✓✓✓✓✓
   Ⓑ ✓✓✓✓✓✓
   Ⓒ ✓✓✓✓✓✓✓
   Ⓓ ✓✓✓✓✓✓✓✓

2. 3, 4, _____, 6
   Ⓐ 7   Ⓒ 2
   ● 5   Ⓓ 1

3.
   Ⓐ 3   Ⓒ 5
   Ⓑ 4   ● 6

Directions Have children: ★ fill in the bubble next to the picture that shows 7 raindrops; ✦ fill in the bubble next to the missing number; ✪ fill in the bubble next to the number that tells how many animals in all.

11-3

Copyright © Pearson Education, Inc., or its affiliates. All Rights Reserved. K

Content Reviewed

Exercise 1   Count and Recognize a Number of Objects

Exercise 2   Ordering Numbers

Exercise 3   Represent Addition Situations

Also available in print

 30 min # Problem-Based Interactive Learning

Overview Children will use ten-frames and equations to represent the decomposition of 14, 15, and 16 as ten ones and some more ones.

Focus How can the parts of 14, 15, and 16 be represented as 10 ones, or one ten, and some more ones?

Materials Counters (or Teaching Tool 32)

Set the Purpose Remind children that they have learned how to break the numbers 11, 12, and 13 into one ten, which is made up of ten ones, and some additional ones using a double ten-frame. *Today, you will break apart the numbers 14, 15, and 16 into one ten and some more ones.*

Connect Hold up both hands and extend all 10 of your fingers. Ask a volunteer to stand beside you and show 5 fingers. *How many fingers do we have in all?* [15] *How many fingers am I showing?* [10] *How many more fingers are there?* [5]

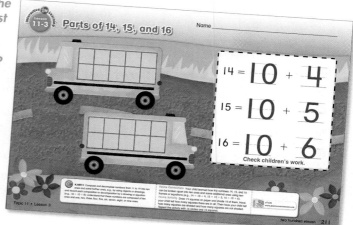

MATHEMATICAL PRACTICES

Communicate
Ask children to explain what the numbers in each number sentence represent.

Pose the Problem *15 kindergartners are going to the zoo. The first bus fills up so the leftover children that couldn't fit on the first bus go on the second bus. How many children are on the first bus? How many children are on the second bus? How can we use ten-frames and a number sentence to describe this situation?* Have children share ideas.

Model *How many children are going to the zoo?* [15] *Let's use counters to show the children.* Fill the first ten-frame on the workmat with 10 counters. Have children do the same. *How many children are on the first bus?* [10] *How many children need to go on the second bus?* [5] Place 5 counters in the second ten-frame and have children do the same. *How many children are there on both buses?* [15] *What number does the first ten-frame show?* [10] *What number does the second ten-frame show?* [5] *What number sentence should we write?* [15 = 10 + 5] Check that children have placed the correct number of counters in each ten-frame and completed the number sentence.

Small-Group Interaction Have partners work together to fill in the ten-frames and complete the number sentences as you pose similar problems about 14 children and 16 children. Ask children questions to help guide their work. *How could you break 14 apart into two groups, with one group of ten? How many counters will you put in the first ten-frame? How many additional ones will go in the second ten-frame? What number sentence will you write?* [Answers will vary.]

How many more children would it take to fill the second bus if there are 14 children now? [6 more] *How many more children would it take to fill the second bus if there are 15 children now?* [5 more] *What stays the same from 14 to 15?* [The 10] *What changes?* [the number of additional ones] *How many more children would it take if there are 16 children now?* [4 more]

Visual Learning

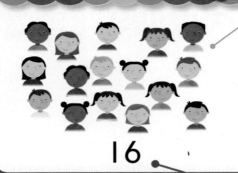

16

What do you know? [There are 16 children.] *Each bus holds 10 students. They need 2 buses. Why do they need 2 buses?* [16 is more than 10.]

How many children are on the first bus? [10] *How many children are on the second bus?* [6] *How many empty seats are on the second bus?* [4]

1 Visual Learning

Set the Purpose Call children's attention to the Visual Learning Bridge at the top of the page. *In this lesson, you will learn to break 14, 15, and 16 into two parts where one part is always 10.*

2 Guided Practice

Remind children each counter shows 1 in the ten-frame. When they count the counters in the ten-frame, it should match the number they are working with.

Error Intervention

If children place the counters randomly in the second ten-frame,

then show them that even though their answer shows the same number of counters, it is hard to quickly count them if they are not in order. Suggest they start along the top line of the second ten-frame.

Do you understand? Have students describe how to break 14, 15, or 16 into parts, with 10 as one part. [Count out the number of counters. Completely fill up a ten-frame and then use the extra counters to begin a new one.]

Reteaching On the board, write 14, 15, or 16. Model writing the appropriate number sentence by first creating two ten-frames.

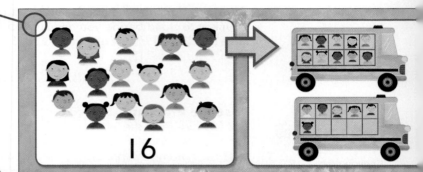

16

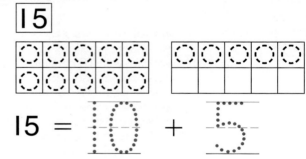

1 15

$$15 = 10 + 5$$

2 14

$$14 = 10 + 4$$

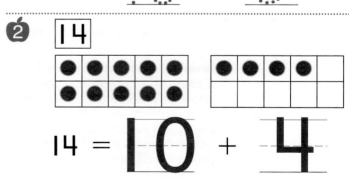

Directions Have children: **1.** trace the counters in the ten-frames to show 15 and trace the number sentence to match the drawing; **2.** draw counters in the ten-frames to show 14 and complete the number sentence to match the drawing.

Topic 11 • Lesson 3

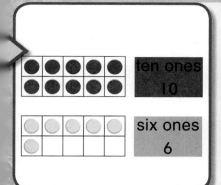

How is this drawing like the bus picture? [It shows 10 in the first ten-frame and 6 in the second ten-frame.] *What does ten ones or 10 describe?* [How many children are on the first bus.] *What does six ones or 6 describe?* [How many children are on the second bus.]

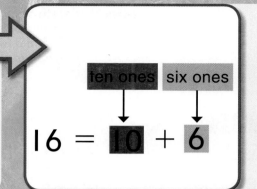

How can 16 be written in two parts? [16 can be written as ten ones and 6 ones.] *What does the 16 represent?* [The number of children in all] *How many children are in the first group?* [10] *How many children are in the second group?* [6]

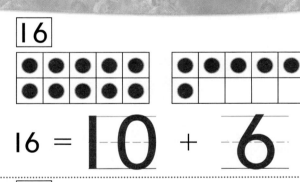

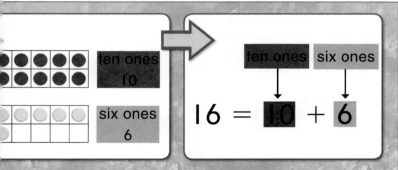

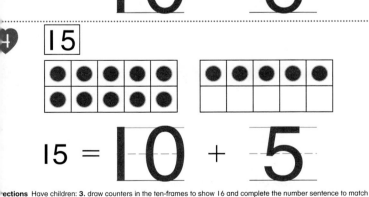

3 ☐16

$$16 = 10 + 6$$

4 ☐15

$$15 = 10 + 5$$

Directions Have children: **3.** draw counters in the ten-frames to show 16 and complete the number sentence to match the drawing; **4.** draw counters in the ten-frames to show 15 and complete the number sentence to match the drawing.

two hundred twelve 212

3 Independent Practice

Children represent 16 and 15 using counters and number sentences.

Close

Essential Understanding The numbers 14, 15, and 16 can be decomposed as the sum of ten ones and four, five, or six ones. *You can break apart 14, 15, and 16 into two groups where one group is 10. A number sentence can be written to show the two groups.*

 ASSESSMENT

Exercise 1 is worth 1 point.
Use the rubric to score Exercise 2.

Exercise 2

Model with Mathematics Children should be able to draw counters in the ten-frames to show 16 and write a number sentence.

E L L Use Repetition For children who need additional help, show them how to break apart 15 using ten-frames and a number sentence. Then use the same explanation allowing children to complete the problem.

Student Samples
3-point answer Children correctly complete the ten-frames to show 16 and provide a correct number sentence.

2-point answer Children break apart 16 into two groups, but the groups are not ten ones and 6 more ones. The number sentence matches their picture, but does not match the problem.

1-point answer Children provide pictures of counters in ten-frames, but they do not equal 16. They do not provide a number sentence or the number sentence does not match the problem.

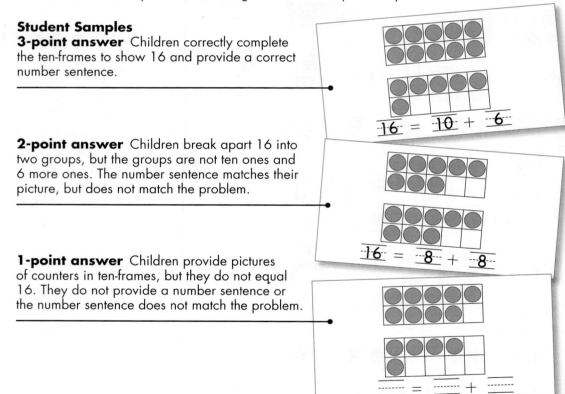

Quick Check Master

Name _____   Quick Check **11-3**

❶

Ⓐ 15 = 7 + 8   Ⓒ 14 = 10 + 4
Ⓑ 15 = 10 + 5   Ⓓ 16 = 10 + 6

❷

_____ = _____ + _____

See students' samples at the right.

Directions Have children: ❶ fill in the bubble next to the number sentence that tells about the ten-frames; ❷ draw counters in the ten-frames to show 16 as one ten and some more ones, then write a number sentence to go with the ten-frames.

 **Formative** Assessment

Use the **Quick Check** to assess children's understanding.

Prescription for Differentiated Instruction

Use children's work on the **Quick Check** to prescribe differentiated instruction.

Points	Prescription
0–2	Intervention
3	On-Level
4	Advanced

Differentiated Instruction

Intervention

Break It Apart

 10–15 min

Materials 16 connecting cubes

- Have children make one long train with the connecting cubes. Discuss how this shows 16.
- Have children break the train so it has 10 cubes on one side and 6 cubes on the other. Discuss how this still shows 16. *What would the 2 trains look like on a ten-frame? How can we use the two trains to write a number sentence?*
- Repeat with a train of 15 cubes and then 14 cubes.

Practice On-Level Center Activity

Practice Advanced Center Activity

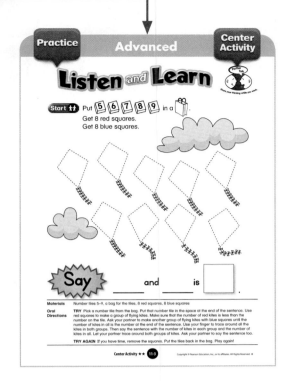

ELL Report Back Listen for the words *in all*. For example, a child might say, "We have 3 blue kites, 4 red kites, and 7 kites *in all*. 3 and 4 is 7."

Leveled Homework

Reteaching Master

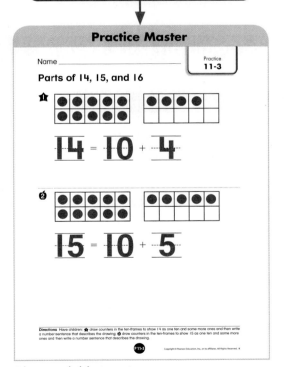

Also available in print

eTools **Counters**
www.pearsonsuccessnet.com

Practice Master

Also available in print

eTools **Counters**
www.pearsonsuccessnet.com

Enrichment Master

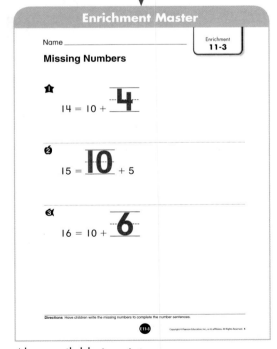

Also available in print

eTools **Counters**
www.pearsonsuccessnet.com

Domain

Number and Operations in Base Ten

Cluster

Work with numbers 11–19 to gain foundations for place value.

Standard

K.NBT.1 Compose and decompose numbers from 11 to 19 into ten ones and some further ones, e.g., by using objects or drawings, and record each composition or decomposition by a drawing or equation (e.g., $18 = 10 + 8$); understand that these numbers are composed of ten ones and one, two, three, four, five, six, seven, eight, or nine ones.

Mathematical Practices

☑ Make sense of problems and persevere in solving them.

☑ Reason abstractly and quantitatively.

◯ Construct viable arguments and critique the reasoning of others.

☑ Model with mathematics.

☑ Use appropriate tools strategically.

☑ Attend to precision.

☑ Look for and make use of structure.

◯ Look for and express regularity in repeated reasoning.

Parts of 17, 18, and 19

 **Lesson Overview**

Objective	Essential Understanding	Vocabulary	Materials
Children will make drawings and write number sentences that represent the decomposition of 17, 18, and 19 into ten and 7, 8, or 9 ones.	Number sentences can be written to represent the decomposition of 17, 18, and 19 as the sum of 10 and 7, 8, or 9 additional ones.		Two-color counters (or Teaching Tool 32), connecting cubes, crayons

PROFESSIONAL DEVELOPMENT

Math Background

The double ten-frame is an especially important tool to think about numbers as large as 17, 18, and 19. In this particular lesson, children start out with a long train of connecting cubes that by their very nature are difficult to count visually. However, the task becomes very easy when the cubes are broken apart and placed in the ten-frames.

Then, because children have used the ten-frames consistently and often, they can immediately see the number as a ten and some ones. With experience, the double ten-frame model is a very appropriate tool for a beginning understanding of place value and the parts of teen numbers.

1 Daily Common Core Review

Daily Common Core Review

Name _____

Daily Common
Core Review
11-4

1

Ⓐ 14 + 1   Ⓒ 14 + 4

Ⓑ 1 + 4   ⬤ 10 + 4

2

⬤ 8 = 3 + 5
Ⓑ 5 = 2 + 3
Ⓒ 8 = 7 + 1
Ⓓ 7 = 3 + 4

Directions Have children mark the best answer. ★ Which number sentence shows the parts of 14? ● Which number sentence describes the fruit?

Also available in print

Content Reviewed

Exercise 1   Parts of 14

Exercise 2   Write Number Sentences for 8

 30 min ## Problem-Based Interactive Learning

Overview Children will represent the decomposition of 17, 18, and 19 into one ten and 7, 8, or 9 ones.

Focus How can the parts of 17, 18, and 19 be represented as a drawing and an equation using one ten and some more ones?

Materials Two-Color Counters (or Teaching Tool 32), connecting cubes in two colors, yellow and red crayons

Set the Purpose Remind children that they have learned how to break apart the numbers 11 to 16 into two parts, with one part being ten ones, or one ten, in each case. Remind them that ten ones are needed to make one ten. *Today, you will be learning how to separate the numbers 17, 18, and 19 into two parts and write number sentences to show what you have done.*

Connect Display a cube train of connecting cubes with 10 blue cubes and 7 red cubes. *How many cubes are there in all?* [17] Separate the cube train into two smaller cube trains by color. *How many cubes are in the blue cube train?* [10] *How many cubes are in the red cube train?* [7] *What number sentence could we write to show this?* [Allow children to share ideas.]

MATHEMATICAL PRACTICES

Use Appropriate Tools
Remind children they can use drawings and objects to model the numbers 17, 18, and 19 as ten and more ones.

Pose the Problem *How many squares are there in the first row on your workmat?* [17] *How could we split 17 into ten ones and some more ones?* Allow children to share ideas before modeling the situation.

Model Place yellow counters in the first 10 spaces in the row of 17 squares at the top of the page. *How many counters are in this group?* [10] *Color the first 10 squares yellow to show 10. Let's fill the rest of the squares with red counters.* Place red counters in the remaining 7 squares. *How many red counters are in this group?* [7] *Color the 7 leftover squares red to show the 7 ones. How can you write a number sentence describing the 17 squares?* Draw children's attention to the 17 in the first number sentence at the top of the page. *What does this number describe?* [The total number of squares in the row] *What number should we write next?* [10] *What number goes last?* [7] Have children complete the number sentence.

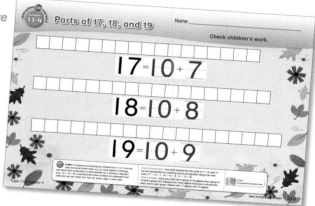

Small-Group Interaction Have pairs of children work together to color in the remaining rows of squares with yellow and red crayons and complete the number sentences for 18 and 19. Children should color the first 10 squares one color, and the remaining squares with another color. Ask guiding questions to facilitate their work. *How many ones are in the first group?* [10] *How many ones are in the second group?* [Answers will vary.] Facilitate their work by asking questions. *How does your number sentence tell about your squares?* Encourage children to see how the number sentences relate to 17, 18, and 19 as the sum of 10 ones, or one ten, and 7, 8, or 9 more ones.

Remind children about the cube trains used in the Connect section. *How could we use a double ten-frame to break the cube train apart?* [We could put the 10 blue cubes into one ten-frame and the red cubes into the second ten-frame.] *What number sentence could you write then?* [We could write a number sentence that would say ten plus the number of ones in the second ten-frame.] *What number would start your number sentence?* [The total number of cubes]

eTools **Counters**
www.pearsonsuccessnet.com

Visual Learning

17

Billy had a cube train. How many cubes long was his cube train? [17] *Why is the number 17 shown?* [Because there are 17 cubes]

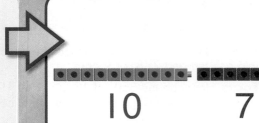

10   7

Billy broke apart his cube train into two groups. How many blue cubes are there? [10] *How many red cubes are there?* [7]

1 Visual Learning

Set the Purpose Call children's attention to the Visual Learning Bridge at the top of the page. *In this lesson, you will learn how to break apart 17, 18, and 19 into one ten and some additional ones.*

2 Guided Practice

Remind children to use the ten-frames to help them decompose 17, 18, and 19 into one ten, or ten ones, and seven, eight, or nine additional ones.

Error Intervention

If children have difficulty drawing the correct number of squares,

then have them work with counters and a double ten-frame (Teaching Tool 9). Remind them to fill the first ten-frame to make one ten and put the remaining ones in the second ten-frame.

Do you understand? *How can you break apart a teen number into one ten and some more ones, make a drawing, and write a number sentence to describe it?* [Make two parts and include one part that is ten. Draw 10 counters in one ten-frame and more ones in the other ten-frame. Write a number sentence in the form ___ = 10 + ___.]

Reteaching Give pairs of children a double ten-frame and 18 two-color counters. Have children put 10 red counters in the first ten-frame. Then have them put 8 yellow counters in the second ten-frame. *How many counters are there in all?* [18] *How many red counters are there?* [10] *How many yellow counters are there?* [8] Write 18 = 10 + 8 on the board.

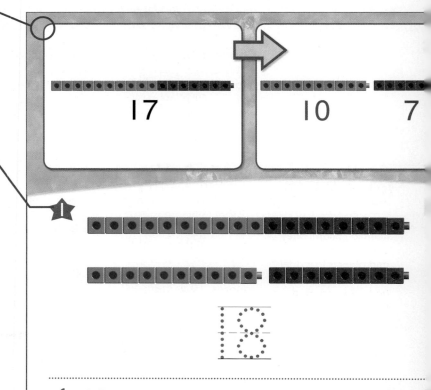

17

10   7

8

Children should draw 10 blue squares.   **Children should draw 9 red squares.**

19 = 10 + 9

Directions Provide children with red and blue crayons. Have children: **1.** count the red and blue cubes. Have children trace the number that shows how many cubes there are in all; **2.** draw red and blue squares in the ten-frames to match the number sentence.

Topic 11 • Lesson 4

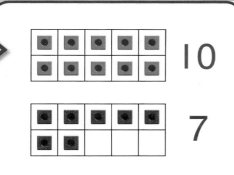

Billy put cubes in the ten-frames. How many cubes did Billy put in the top ten-frame? [10] How many cubes did he put in the bottom ten-frame? [7] How many cubes are there in all? [17]

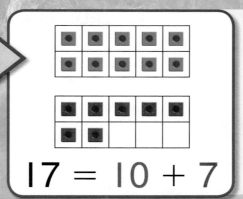

Does this number sentence match the cubes? [Yes] What does the number 17 represent? [The number of cubes in all] What does the 10 represent? [The cubes in the top ten-frame] What does the 7 represent? [The cubes in the bottom ten-frame]

$17 = 10 + 7$

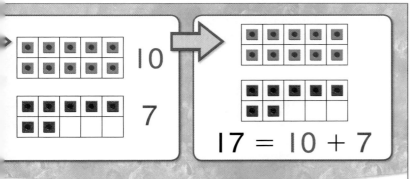

$17 = 10 + 7$

3

Children should draw 10 blue squares and 7 red squares.

17

4

Children should draw 10 blue squares.

Children should draw 8 red squares.

$18 = 10 + 8$

Directions Provide children with red and blue crayons. Have children: **3.** color the squares so that 10 are blue and the rest are red. Have children write how many squares are colored in all; **4.** draw red and blue squares in the ten-frames to match the number sentence.

two hundred fourteen 214

Additional Activity

Domino Draw

🕐 10 min 👥

Materials Index cards, dot stickers

- Children make dominoes for 17, 18, and 19 using dot stickers and index cards as shown below:

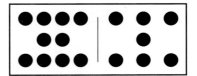

This is a domino for 17.

17 = 10 + 7

- Dominoes can also be made as ten-frame parts with a completed ten-frame on one side and the additional ones on the other side.

- After the dominoes have been made, children can work with a partner and read each domino as one ten and some more ones.

3 Independent Practice

Children color squares so ten are blue and the rest are red and write the number of squares in all. They draw blue and red squares in the ten-frames to match the number sentence.

Close

Essential Understanding Number sentences can be written to represent 17, 18, and 19 as one ten and some ones. *Remember that you can represent the decomposition of 17, 18, and 19 as one ten, or ten ones, and some more ones with a drawing or number sentence.*

 **ASSESSMENT**

Exercise 1 is worth 1 point.
Use the rubric to score Exercise 2.

Exercise 2
Model with Mathematics Children should be able to show 19 as one ten and 9 ones coloring squares in the ten-frames to match the number sentence.

ELL Rephrase For children who need additional help understanding or following the directions, rephrase the question in a different way to ensure they clearly understand the task.

Student Samples
3-point answer Children correctly show 10 squares in the first ten-frame and 9 squares in the second ten-frame.

2-point answer Children correctly show 10 squares in the first ten-frame and show some ones in the second ten-frame.

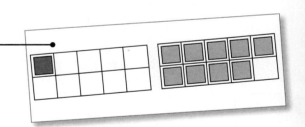

1-point answer Children do not draw 10 squares in the first ten-frame.

Quick Check Master

Name _____

Quick Check
11-4

❶
Ⓐ 70 + 1
Ⓑ 10 + 7
Ⓒ 1 + 7
Ⓓ 17 + 7

❷

$19 = 10 + 9$

See students' samples at the right.

Directions Have children mark the best answer. ❶ Which shows the parts of 17? ❷ Color squares to match the number sentence.

Copyright © Pearson Education, Inc., or its affiliates. All Rights Reserved.

 **Formative** Assessment

Use the **Quick Check** to assess children's understanding.

Prescription for Differentiated Instruction

Use children's work on the **Quick Check** to prescribe differentiated instruction.

Points	Prescription
0–2	Intervention
3	On-Level
4	Advanced

Differentiated Instruction

Intervention

Number Sentences with 11 to 19

  10 min

Materials (per pair) 2 double ten-frames (or Teaching Tool 9), 9 two-color counters (or Teaching Tool 32), cup, crayons

- Have children color 10 counters in their top ten-frame. *This is one ten.*
- Partners take turns shaking a cup of 9 counters and pouring the contents onto a table. They count how many counters landed yellow or red side up. Partner A places the yellow counters on the bottom of his or her double ten-frame. Partner B places the red counters on the bottom of his or her double ten-frame.
- Partners write number sentences to show the number of counters in all and the groups of ten and ones.

On-Level

Practice | **On-Level** | **Center Activity**

Start Get 1 2 3 4 5 5 6 7 8 9.

Get a 🐞
Get 6 red squares.
Get 6 blue squares.

Say ☐ and ☐ is **10.**

Materials Number tiles 1–9 and 5, one number cube, 6 red squares, 6 blue squares
Oral Directions TRY Toss the cube. Count the dots. Put that number of red squares in the tower. Put a tile at the beginning of the sentence to show how many squares you put in the tower. Ask your partner to use blue squares to finish building the tower. Put a tile in the second space to show the number of squares your partner needs to finish the tower. Count all the squares in the tower. Take turns reading the sentence. Look at the tower and explain what the sentence means.

TRY AGAIN Remove the squares and the number tiles. Play again!

Center Activity ★ 11-4

Advanced

Practice | **Advanced** | **Center Activity**

Start Get 3 4 5 6 6 7 8 9.

Get 9 red squares.
Get 9 blue squares.

Say ☐ and ☐ is **12.**

Materials Number tiles 3–9 and 6, 9 red squares, 9 blue squares
Oral Directions TRY Choose any number tile and put it at the beginning of the sentence. Put that number of red squares in the tower. Ask your partner to use blue squares to finish building the tower. Put a tile in the second space to show the number of squares your partner needs to finish the tower. Count all the squares in the tower. Take turns reading the sentence. Look at the tower and explain what the sentence means.

TRY AGAIN Remove the squares and the number tiles. If you have time, play again!

Center Activity ★★ 11-4

ELL Report Back To check understanding, ask a child to repeat and complete this sentence: *If every space in a first ten-frame is filled and 8 spaces are filled in a second ten-frame, the number in all is _____.* [18]

Leveled Homework

Reteaching Master

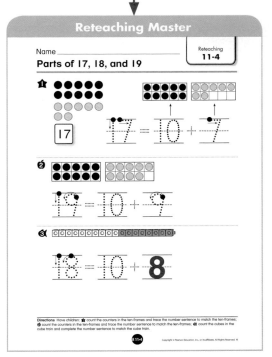

Name _____
Parts of 17, 18, and 19

Reteaching 11-4

Practice Master

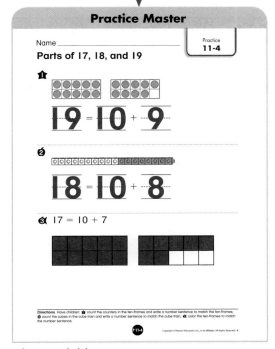

Name _____
Parts of 17, 18, and 19

Practice 11-4

Enrichment Master

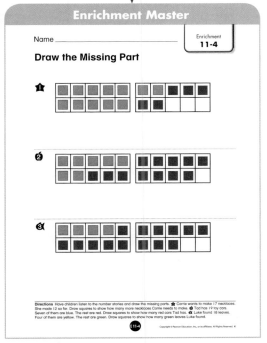

Name _____
Draw the Missing Part

Enrichment 11-4

Also available in print

Also available in print

Also available in print

 eTools **Counters**
www.pearsonsuccessnet.com

 eTools **Counters**
www.pearsonsuccessnet.com

 eTools **Counters**
www.pearsonsuccessnet.com

Problem Solving: Look for a Pattern

Lesson Overview

Objective	Essential Understanding	Vocabulary	Materials
Children will identify patterns found in decomposing the teen numbers, including the constant of one ten and the variable number of ones. They will make drawings and write number sentences for numbers 11 to 19.	Some problems can be solved by identifying elements that repeat in a predictable way.		Counters, crayons, large piece of paper, such as butcher paper

PROFESSIONAL DEVELOPMENT

Math Background

Recognizing patterns and organizing information are part of recognizing structure. To become mathematically proficient, children must learn to identify number patterns. In this place value activity, there are repeating patterns that can be demonstrated by looking at the groupings made in the tens and ones. The repeating pattern demonstrated in the following grouping is foundational to an understanding of the base-ten system and thus an important mathematical practice for young children.

0	1	2	3	4	5	6	7	8	9
10	11	12	13	14	15	16	17	18	19

Common Core

Domain
Number and Operations in Base Ten

Cluster
Work with numbers 11–19 to gain foundations for place value.

Standard
K.NBT.1 Compose and decompose numbers from 11 to 19 into ten ones and some further ones, e.g., by using objects or drawings, and record each composition or decomposition by a drawing or equation (e.g., 18 = 10 + 8); understand that these numbers are composed of ten ones and one, two, three, four, five, six, seven, eight, or nine ones.

Mathematical Practices

☑ Make sense of problems and persevere in solving them.

☑ Reason abstractly and quantitatively.

○ Construct viable arguments and critique the reasoning of others.

☑ Model with mathematics.

○ Use appropriate tools strategically.

○ Attend to precision.

☑ Look for and make use of structure.

☑ Look for and express regularity in repeated reasoning.

1 Daily Common Core Review

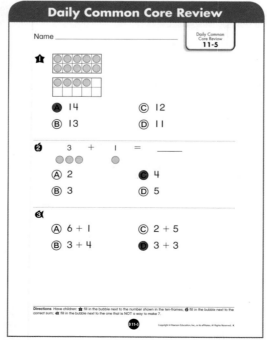

Content Reviewed

Exercise 1   Count 14

Exercise 2   Represent Addition Situations

Exercise 3   Identify Ways to Make 7

Also available in print

MATHEMATICAL PRACTICES

 30 min **Problem-Based Interactive Learning**

Overview Children will look for patterns to help them when decomposing numbers 11 to 19 into a ten and ones.

Focus What patterns can be identified and extended to decompose numbers 11 to 19 into ten and ones?

Materials Butcher paper, (per pair) counters (or Teaching Tool 32), red and blue crayons

Set the Purpose *You have learned how to break apart numbers 11 to 19 into a group of ten ones, or a ten, and a group with some more ones. Today you will learn how to look for patterns to help you decompose numbers and write number sentences.*

Connect *How can you use patterns to help you solve problems?* Have children share ideas.

Pose the Problem *How can we use patterns to break apart numbers 11 to 19 into a ten and ones and write number sentences?* Allow children to share ideas before modeling the situation.

Model Show a piece of butcher paper that has the numbers 11, 12, 13, 14, 15, 16, 17, 18, and 19 written in a vertical line, with 11 at the top and 19 at the bottom. *Today we will be looking for patterns to help us break apart all of these teen numbers into a ten and ones.* Assign each pair one of the numbers 11 to 19. Ask them to count out that number of counters, place 10 of them on the blue ten-frame and the rest on the red ten-frame. Ask each pair to write the number sentence that describes their picture next to their number on the butcher paper with blue and red crayons. Have children use a blue crayon to write the number of counters on the blue ten-frame and a red crayon to write the number of counters on the red ten-frame. *What do you notice about the blue numbers in the number sentences?* [They are always 10.] *What do you notice about the red numbers in the number sentences?* [They go up by 1 each time.]

MATHEMATICAL PRACTICES

Repeated Reasoning
Highlight the colors used on the workmat and the corresponding number sentence portion. Emphasize both the color and number pattern. Focus children's attention on the matching colors of the ten-frames and the number 10 in the number sentences.

Small-Group Interaction Demonstrate how to decompose 17 using directions from the children. *How should we start?* [Count out 17 counters.] *To break 17 apart into a ten and ones, what should we do?* [Fill the blue-ten frame with 10 counters.] *After the blue ten-frame is full, what should we do?* [Put the leftover counters in the red ten-frame.] *What number sentence should we use to describe the drawing we made?* [17 = 10 + 7] Check that children wrote the correct numbers in the appropriate boxes. Repeat the process with other numbers.

 What would the number sentence for 20 look like? [20 = 10 + 10]

DIGITAL eTools **Counters**
www.pearsonsuccessnet.com

Visual Learning

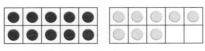

Read and Understand

$18 = 10 + 8$

How do the counters in the ten-frames match the numbers in the number sentence? [The ten-frame with red counters shows a red number 10 in the number sentence. The ten-frame with yellow counters shows a yellow number 8 in the number sentence.]

Plan

$11 = 10 + 1$ $16 = 10 + 6$
$12 = 10 + 2$ $17 = 10 + 7$
$13 = 10 + 3$ $18 = 10 + 8$
$14 = 10 + 4$ _____
$15 = 10 + 5$ _____

$19 = 10 +$ _____

What color and number patterns do you see in these number sentences? [The number 10 is always red. The last number is always yellow. The black and yellow numbers always grow by 1.] *How can you use patterns to help you solve the problem?* [Have children share ideas.]

---

1 Visual Learning

Set the Purpose Call children's attention to the **Visual Learning Bridge** at the top of the page. *In this lesson, you will look for patterns to break apart numbers from 11 to 19.*

2 Guided Practice

Remind children to use counters to help them solve the problems.

Error Intervention
If children have difficulty writing the correct numbers,

then have them use a red crayon to write the number 10 and a yellow crayon to write the number of additional ones. Help them see how the numbers in the number sentence relate to the counters.

Do you understand? *How can you describe the pattern used to break apart 19?* [Completely fill up one ten-frame. Then use the leftover counters in the second ten-frame. Write 10 for the full ten-frame. Write the leftover counters as ones.]

Reteaching On the board, write 16. Model breaking apart the number into one ten and ones using ten-frames and counters.

Read and Understand

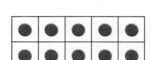

$18 = 10 + 8$

Plan

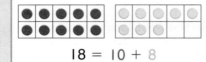
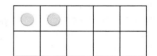

$11 = 10 + 1$ $16 = 10 +$
$12 = 10 + 2$ $17 = 10 +$
$13 = 10 + 3$ $18 = 10 +$
$14 = 10 + 4$
$15 = 10 + 5$

$19 = 10 +$ __

1

$12 = 10 + 2$

2

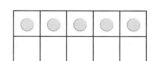

$15 = 10 + 5$

Directions Have children look at the ten-frames and then: **1.** trace the numbers that complete the number sentence; **2.** write the numbers that complete the number sentence to show 15.

Topic 11 • Lesson 5

Solve

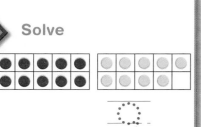

$$19 = 10 + \underline{9}$$

How many counters are there in all? [19] *How many red counters are there?* [10] *How many yellow counters are there?* [9] *What number should we write to complete the number sentence?* [9] *What color should the number 9 be?* [Yellow]

 Look Back and Check

$11 = 10 + 1$	$16 = 10 + 6$
$12 = 10 + 2$	$17 = 10 + 7$
$13 = 10 + 3$	$18 = 10 + 8$
$14 = 10 + 4$	$19 = 10 + 9$
$15 = 10 + 5$	

Look at the last number sentence. How can you check your answer? [Use the patterns] *Does it match the patterns? How?* [Yes. The number 10 is red. The number 9 is yellow. The black and yellow numbers are 1 more than the numbers in the sentence before it.]

Solve

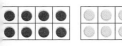

$$19 = 10 + \underline{9}$$

 Look Back and Check

$11 = 10 + 1$	$16 = 10 + 6$
$12 = 10 + 2$	$17 = 10 + 7$
$13 = 10 + 3$	$18 = 10 + 8$
$14 = 10 + 4$	$19 = 10 + 9$
$15 = 10 + 5$	

 3

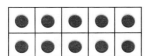

$$17 = 10 + 7$$

 4

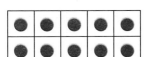

$$14 = 10 + 4$$

Directions Have children look at the ten-frames and then: **3.** write the numbers that complete the number sentence; **4.** write the numbers that complete the number sentence.

two hundred sixteen **216**

Additional Activity

Full and Empty Patterns

🕐 10–15 min

Materials 9 index cards

- Draw 2 ten-frames on each card. Then fill in the ten-frames to represent each of the numbers 11 to 19.
- Place the ten-frame cards in order from 11 to 19.
- For each card, have children identify the number of spaces that are full and the number of spaces that are empty.

  11 has 11 spaces filled and 9 spaces empty.

  12 has 12 spaces filled and 8 spaces empty.

  13 has 13 spaces filled and 7 spaces empty.

  14 has 14 spaces filled and 6 spaces empty.

  15 has 15 spaces filled and 5 spaces empty.

  16 has 16 spaces filled and 4 spaces empty.

  17 has 17 spaces filled and 3 spaces empty.

  18 has 18 spaces filled and 2 spaces empty.

  19 has 19 spaces filled and 1 space empty.

- Have children identify any patterns they see in the number of spaces filled and the number of spaces empty.

3 **Independent Practice** © **MATHEMATICAL PRACTICES**

© **Use Structure** Children use ten-frames and number sentences to represent the parts of numbers 11 to 19.

Close

Essential Understanding *When breaking apart the numbers 11 to 19, you can use ten-frames and look for a pattern to create number sentences.*

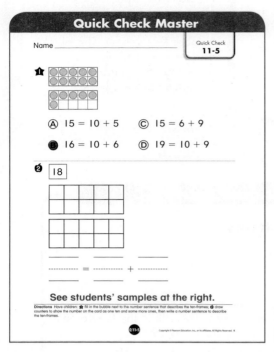

Formative Assessment

Use the **Quick Check** to assess children's understanding.

 **ASSESSMENT**

Exercise 1 is worth 1 point.
Use the rubric to score Exercise 2.

Exercise 2

Repeated Reasoning Children should be able to draw the correct number of counters in the ten-frames and write the corresponding number sentence to show 18.

ELL Model Thinking Aloud For children who need additional help organizing their thinking, have them describe aloud the steps they are using to solve the problem.

Student Samples
3-point answer Children draw 18 counters as a ten and 8 ones and write the correct corresponding number sentence.

2-point answer Children draw 18 counters as a ten and 8 ones but do not write the correct corresponding number sentence.

1-point answer Children draw an incorrect number of counters. They do not write a number sentence or the number sentence does not match the problem.

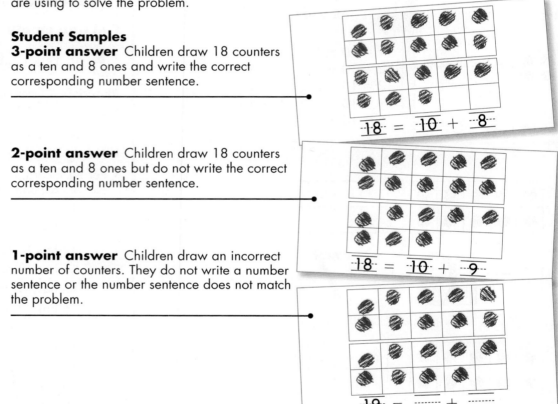

Prescription for Differentiated Instruction

Use children's work on the **Quick Check** to prescribe differentiated instruction.

Points	Prescription
0–2	Intervention
3	On-Level
4	Advanced

Differentiated Instruction

Intervention

Take Turns

 10–15 min

Materials (per pair) 2 ten-frames, counters

- Choose a number from 11 to 19.
- Have children take turns placing counters in the ten-frames to make the number.
- Then have one child point to the ten-frame while the other child records the appropriate number in the number sentence.
- Repeat for other numbers.

On-Level
Practice **Center Activity**

Helping Hands

Start ↑↑ Put 1 2 3 4 5 in a 📖
Get 9 red squares.

☐ + ☐ = ☐

Materials: Number tiles 1–5, a bag for the tiles, 9 red squares

Oral Directions: **TRY** Pick a tile. Put it to the left of the plus sign. Count that number of squares. Then your partner picks a tile, puts it to the right of the plus sign, and counts that number of squares. Pretend your squares are pieces of cheese. Put all of the pieces of cheese on the plate. Find out how many there are in all. Say the sum. Use your finger to trace in the air. Trace the first number, then the plus sign, the second number, then the equal sign, and then the sum. Trace the number sentence in the air three times. Watch as your partner traces the number sentence in the air three times.

TRY AGAIN If you have time, put the tiles back in the bag. Remove the squares. Play again!

Center Activity ★ 11-5   Copyright © Pearson Education, Inc., or its affiliates. All Rights Reserved. K

Advanced
Practice **Center Activity**

Helping Hands

Start ↑↑ Get 3 4 5 6 7 8 9.
Get 12 red squares.

☐ + ☐ = 12

Materials: Number tiles 3–9 and 6, 12 red squares

Oral Directions: **TRY** Pretend your squares are pieces of cheese. One partner puts a number tile to the left of the plus sign, and then puts that number of pieces of cheese on the plate. Decide how many more pieces of cheese you need so that there will be twelve pieces of cheese on the plate in all. Put those pieces of cheese on the plate and show that number with a tile to the right of the plus sign. Say the number sentence. Use your finger to trace in the air. Trace the first number, then the plus sign, the second number, then the equal sign, and then the sum. Trace the number sentence in the air three times. Watch as your partner traces the number sentence in the air three times.

TRY AGAIN If you have time, remove the tiles and the squares. Play again!

Center Activity ★★ 11-5   Copyright © Pearson Education, Inc., or its affiliates. All Rights Reserved. K

ELL Partner Talk Listen for the words *in all*. For example, a child might say, "We have 12 *in all*."

Leveled Homework

Reteaching Master

Name _____ Reteaching 11-5

Problem Solving: Look for a Pattern

① 18 = 10 + 8

② 14 = 10 + 4

③ 16 = 10 + 6

Directions Have children: ★ trace 18 counters in the ten-frames and complete the number sentence; ❷ trace 14 counters in the ten-frames and complete the number sentence; ❸ draw the counters in the second ten-frame to show 16 and complete the number sentence.

R 11-5   Copyright © Pearson Education, Inc., or its affiliates. K

Also available in print

Practice Master

Name _____ Practice 11-5

Problem Solving: Look for a Pattern

① 15 = 10 + 5

② 19 = 10 + 9

③ 17 = 10 + 7

Directions Have children: ★ draw 15 counters as one ten, or ten ones, and some additional ones and then complete the number sentence; ❷ draw 19 counters as one ten, or ten ones, and some additional ones and then complete the number sentence; ❸ look at the counters and write a number sentence to match the picture.

P 11-5   Copyright © Pearson Education, Inc., or its affiliates. K

Also available in print

Enrichment Master

Name _____ Enrichment 11-5

Take Away

① 14

② 17

③ 12

Directions Have children decide how many counters need to be taken away from the ten-frames to show each number. Have children mark Xs on the extra counters.

E 11-5   Copyright © Pearson Education, Inc., or its affiliates. K

Also available in print

Reteaching

INTERVENTION

Name _____

Set A

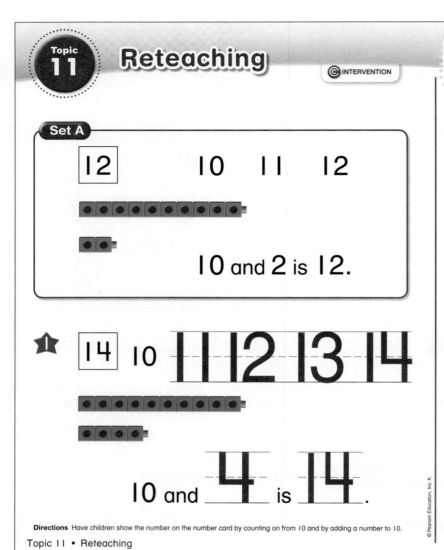

12   10   11   12

10 and 2 is 12.

Set B

13 = 10 + 3

① 14 10 11 12 13 14

10 and **4** is **14**.

②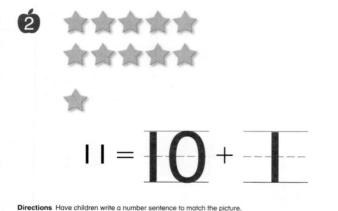

11 = 10 + 1

Directions Have children show the number on the number card by counting on from 10 and by adding a number to 10.

Topic 11 • Reteaching

Directions Have children write a number sentence to match the picture.

© Pearson Education, Inc. K

two hundred seventeen   217

Purpose

- Provide children with more examples and practice for each lesson in the topic.

- For intervention materials, use the resources listed in the chart to the right.

RTI

Item Analysis for Diagnosis and Intervention

Objective	Common Core Standards	Reteaching Sets	Student Book Lessons	Intervention System
Use objects to create sets to 19.	K.NBT.1	Set A	11-1	
Write equations that represent the decomposition of 11, 12, and 13 as a ten and some ones.	K.NBT.1	Set B	11-2	A14
Write equations that represent the decomposition of 14, 15, and 16 as a ten and some ones.	K.NBT.1	Set C	11-3	A14
Write equations that represent the decomposition of 17, 18, and 19 as a ten and some ones.	K.NBT.1	Set D	11-4	A14

 Topic 11 **Reteaching** Ⓒ INTERVENTION

Set C

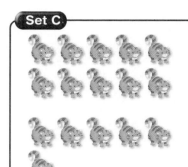

$$16 = 10 + 6$$

Set D

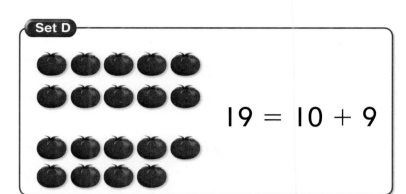

$$19 = 10 + 9$$

3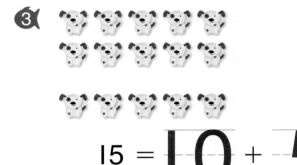

$$15 = 10 + 5$$

4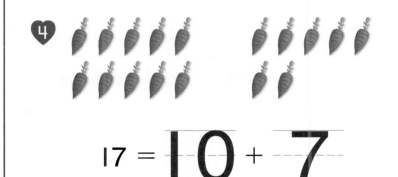

$$17 = 10 + 7$$

Directions Have children complete the number sentence to match the picture.

Directions Have children complete the number sentence to match the picture.

Topic 11 • Reteaching

© Pearson Education, Inc. K

two hundred eighteen **218**

Response to Intervention

 RTI
TIER **1**
ONGOING

Ongoing Intervention
- Lessons with guiding questions to assess understanding
- Support to prevent misconceptions and to reteach

 RTI
TIER **2**
STRATEGIC

Strategic Intervention
- Targeted to small groups who need more support
- Easy to implement

 RTI
TIER **3**
INTENSIVE

Intensive Intervention
- Instruction to accelerate progress
- Instruction focused on foundational skills

Topic 11 **Test** ⓒ ASSESSMENT

Name _____

 1

Ⓐ 10 and 3 is 13.   Ⓒ 10 and 2 is 12.

Ⓑ 10 and 5 is 15.   Ⓓ 10 and 4 is 14.

 2

Ⓐ 14 = 10 + 4   Ⓒ 12 = 10 + 2

Ⓑ 13 = 10 + 3   Ⓓ 11 = 10 + 1

3

Ⓐ 16   Ⓒ 18

Ⓑ 17   Ⓓ 19

 4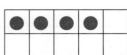

$14 = 10 + 4$

 5 19

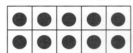 

$19 = 10 + 9$

Multiple-Choice Directions Have children mark the best answer. **1.** Which tells about the ten-frames in the picture? **2.** Which number sentence tells about the counters? **3.** How many squares are there in all?

Constructed-Response Directions Have children: **4.** draw counters in the ten-frames to show 14 and complete the number sentence to match the drawings; **5.** draw 19 counters in the ten-frames and complete the number sentence to match the drawings.

Topic 11 • Test

two hundred nineteen **219**

Purpose
- Assess children's understanding of the concepts and skills in Topic 11 using multiple-choice and constructed-response formats.
- Additional assessment options can be found in the Teacher Resource Masters.
- For intervention materials that correspond to all tests, use the resources listed in the chart on the next page.

Test-Taking Tips

Discuss with children the following tips for test success.

Understand the Question
- Look for important words.
- Turn the question into a statement: "I need to find out…"

Gather Information
- Get information from text.
- Get information from pictures, maps, diagrams, tables, and graphs.

Make a Plan
- Think about problem-solving skills and strategies.
- Choose computation methods.

Make Smart Choices
- Eliminate wrong answers.
- Try working backward from an answer.
- Check answers for reasonableness; estimate.

Item Analysis for Diagnosis and Intervention

Objective	© Common Core Standards	Test Items	Student Book Lessons	Intervention System
Use objects to create sets to 19.	**K.NBT.1**	1	11-1	
Write equations that represent the decomposition of 11, 12, and 13 as a ten and some ones.	**K.NBT.1**	2	11-2	A14
Solve problems by identifying repeating elements.	**K.NBT.1**	3	11-5	A14
Write equations that represent the decomposition of 14, 15, and 16 as a ten and some ones.	**K.NBT.1**	4	11-3	A14
Write equations that represent the decomposition of 17, 18, and 19 as a ten and some ones.	**K.NBT.1**	5	11-4	A14

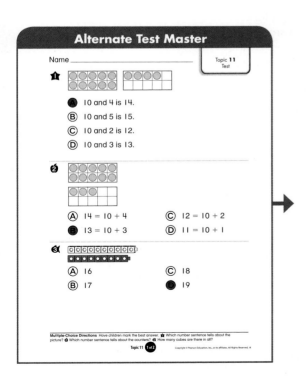

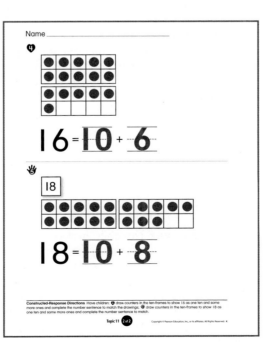

 ASSESSMENT

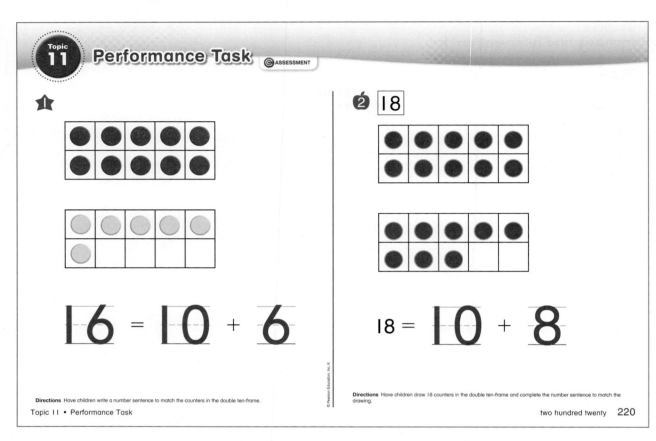

Purpose Assess children's understanding of concepts and skills in Topic 11 through a performance-based task.

Task For this assessment, children write an addition number sentence to match counters shown in a double ten-frame. Then children draw counters in a double ten-frame and complete a number sentence to match what they drew.

Get Ready Review how to show numbers 11 to 19 in a double ten-frame and how to write a matching number sentence.

Guiding the Activity Remind children that the total number of counters in each double ten-frame is the "whole," or the first number of the number sentence they are writing. The number of counters in the top ten-frame and the number of counters in the bottom ten-frame are the "parts," or the other two numbers of the number sentence. For Part 2, you may allow children to trace counters on the double ten-frame.

Questioning Strategies How many counters are there in all? How many counters are in each part of the double ten-frame? How do the counters in each double ten-frame help you write each number sentence?

Scoring Rubric

3-Point answer The child writes the correct number sentence in Part 1. In Part 2, the child draws 18 counters in the correct arrangement in the double ten-frame and completes the number sentence correctly.

2-Point answer The child makes minor errors when writing the number sentences or decomposes the numbers 16 and 18 in a way that does not match the counters. In Part 2, the child draws a total of 18 counters, but they are not correctly placed within the double ten-frame.

1-Point answer The child writes incorrect number sentences or number sentences that do not correspond to the counters in the double ten-frames. The child has difficulty understanding how to draw counters within a double ten-frame or draws an incorrect number of counters.